BROTHER JUNIPER STRIKES AGAIN

Books by Father Justin McCarthy

BROTHER JUNIPER

MORE BROTHER JUNIPER

BROTHER JUNIPER STRIKES AGAIN

Brother Juniper Strikes Again

Father Justin McCarthy, O.F.M.

HANOVER HOUSE, GARDEN CITY, NEW YORK

This book is affectionately dedicated to
THE FRANCISCAN FAMILY

Nice things traditionally come in small packages, and the nicest small package we know is Brother Juniper, a newsprint half-pint who daily captivates twenty million followers of the funnies.

We've been puzzling over the multitudinous reasons for the little fellow's popularity and have come up with what we consider a workmanlike solution: People *like* him . . . all kinds of people . . . and for any number of reasons.

An index to his popularity is the flood of mail which pours in from around the country in praise of B.J. Cartoon ideas come from Bishops and Monsignori. Ministers and Rabbis beg him for "originals." Oldsters pen appreciative notes. Teen-agers and tots write fan letters.

Because of this burgeoning affection it is not surprising that his face and figure now appear on cups and saucers, figurines, plates, planters, clocks, and children's lamps. In the works: a Sunday comic strip in full color, Brother Juniper wallpaper, a Brother Juniper movie. Putting it mildly, the little man is a whopping success. Which might prompt one to ask: Will success spoil B.J.? It hasn't—and, say we, who know the man, it won't. B.J. will always be B.J.—wholesome, happy, humble, without guile. Every dime he earns he gives to charity.

While banking accolades about his brow, we would be remiss did we not make mention of the cleric who created him and sustains him daily on his high plateau of rare good humor. "Let Brother Juniper take the bows," says his busy mentor, Father Mac—"but while you're at it, won't you please applaud my assistant, Mr. Len Reno, who does the beautiful finished drawings from my basic roughs. To him should go the lion's share of credit for the panel's success."

Be that as it may, Father Mac's own drawings, done with an incredibly swift left hand ("Fastest draw in the East," he says with a smile) in conjunction with his swift-paced dialogue make him one of the most sought-after religious speakers on the lecture circuit, where his listeners are instantly struck by a mutual resemblance. "*He's* Brother Juniper!" they declare.

The Publishers

7

BROTHER JUNIPER STRIKES AGAIN

"Stop me if you've heard this one . . ."

"It's hard to tell if they have honest faces when they wear masks."

"Yessir, Brother, I think I have something right up
your alley."

13

"Stop whistling? Who, me?"

"What kind of a PLATE do I want? Oh, anything good—how about Wedgwood?"

15

"Chief, he says he'll buy a ticket to the Policeman's Ball if you'll buy one to the Parish Picnic."

16

"I said, do you have 'Silent Night'?"

"Looks like a bad case of housemaid's knee. Do much kneeling?"

18

"*Just answer me one question. Was it done in*
SELF-DEFENSE?"

"That's not the speed limit, that's the route number!"

"I have wonderful news, Spike. They plan to retire
your number when you graduate."

"No, I insist. AFTER YOU!"

23

"Psst . . . We're on!"

"What did I do wrong?"

"A little to your right!"

"These cold mornings I like to serve them toast and coffee."

"Give me two quarts of your fortified milk."

"Well, there's another pressure cooker you've put
in orbit!"

"*Both feet planted firmly in midair as usual.*"

"This oyster stew IS pretty gamey!"

31

"Mind a suggestion, Junior?"

"Ah . . . uh . . . oh, give me a closed Sunday, please."

"Be sure and write when you reach Miami."

"Just as I suspected . . . TERMITES!"

"Matter of fact, sir, my name IS Daniel."

"Hey, only one swing to a pitch!"

39

"Like they say, cleanliness is next to Godliness."

"I'll be all right in a minute. High prices always
make me dizzy."

41

"There but for the grace of God go I!"

"Yours just have no character whatsoever!"

"Weddings always make me cry, too, ma'am!"

"It's easy! First you shoot the arrow, then you just
take your paint brush and . . ."

"Did you ever TRY going straight?"

"You see, sir, I just don't feel that I belong."

"Better light only ONE candle tonight . . . Supper's
pretty bad if I do say so myself!"

"Try this hole for size, kiddo."

"Now watch! This is a rabbit with a big nose who
needs a haircut."

"I'll drive, you bail."

"I'd appreciate it if you'd wipe your big cubic feet
before walking on my nice clean cellar floor."

53

"He can do a better job on himself than anybody
I know."

"When I bring home a stray cat I don't fool around."

"... And for double yolks you get time and a half!"

"I have a new job. I've been kicked upstairs."

"His insurance must be all paid up!"

"Just act supernatural."

"It's a very poor day for drying."

"The new chaplain is a friendly chap. Always calls me by my first number."

"Please, no self-portraits in the shrubbery!"

63

"Oh, just say: Homemaker."

"He's too small for the poultry contest. Why not enter him in the songbird competition?"

"Sure, I get its meaning. It keeps telling me I haven't eaten since breakfast."

"I can see now why they call you a beast of burden!"

"Somehow this dampness goes right through me today."

"Now let's have a nice big frown."

"That new paper boy certainly has a great arm!"

"Around here we always take in the sidewalks at
eight o'clock."

"There were plenty of things you needed more than
a Chinese back-scratcher!"

74

"Brother Juniper, I want you to consider me as a sort of guardian angel."

"We better pay that electric bill. The candle company says no more credit."

"Give me a vanilla cone, please, but don't pack it
down tight . . . I'm on a diet."

"But, Officer, I know for a fact he's OVER 16!"

"Take it slow. The life you save may be MINE!"

"Hello, Acme Barbers' College? Would you please
send over one of your seniors?"

"*Ain't nobody up here but us chickens.*"

"I must have taken a thorn out of his foot at some time or other."

"Care to have a drag race, sonny?"

"Like this, see!"

"Looks like a nervous breakdown to me!"

"I keep telling myself there's no such thing as
a bad boy."

"Canst thou take it off tackle again, Brother Juniper?"

"Somebody better choose Brother Juniper. It's HIS
tire pump!"

"Do you have any GOODminton sets?"

"Of course we're lost! But we're making such good time, let's keep on going!"

"Personally, I like his looks!"

"Aren't you spreading yourself a bit thin?"

"*Either get bigger cups or get a smaller coffeepot!*"

"Oh, it's just a spinach sandwich with ketchup, mustard, and strawberries. Why?"

97

"Remember, if we get lost, we'll all come in together on 'Mother Machree.'"

"This is terrible! We're all out of leftovers!"

"No, thanks. Just sniffing."

"Well, so long. I have to make tracks."

"The cat's safe, but call the Fire Department to get
Brother Juniper down."

"Watch it! I just waxed those flagstones."

"That sticker tells me you bought Girl Scout cookies;
it says nothing about having the car inspected!"

"Well, you certainly don't leave much to Divine
Providence."

"I haven't the heart to tell him it's only poison ivy."

"Nice try!"

"*Good heavens, we forgot Brother Juniper!*"

"Excuse me, lady, I thought I was watering the flowers."

"Here comes God's gift to the corn borers."

"Gee, thanks for listenin' to my troubles."

"It should be just about time to unbend the hose."

"It must be milking time."

"I'd like something for someone who is morally
bankrupt."

"If you could only pick 'em as fast as you can eat 'em!"

"Well, be good."

"Him and his lightning bugs!"

"I changed the spark plugs and took some dents
out of the flying buttresses."

"Why not look upon it as an investment in the future?"

"That's not charcoal. Those are the STEAKS!"

"Hey, Brother Charlie, the Chief's lawn chair
is here!"

"Got everything? Milk, crackers, butter, salt, crackers, coffee . . . crackers?"

"They went thataway!"